Scott, Foresman Reading

Hang On To Your Hats

Program Authors

Ira E. Aaron
Dauris Jackson
Carole Riggs
Richard G. Smith
Robert J. Tierney

Book Authors

Louise Gorgos Botko
JoAnn Krebs Heryla
Verla Kroeker Klassen
John Manning

Instructional Consultants

John Manning
Dolores Perez

Scott, Foresman and Company
Editorial Offices: Glenview, Illinois

Regional Offices: Palo Alto, California
Tucker, Georgia • Glenview, Illinois
Oakland, New Jersey • Dallas, Texas

ACKNOWLEDGMENTS

"My Uncle's Garden" by Kay Douglas from HELLO, PEOPLE by Leland B. Jacobs. Copyright 1972 by Leland B. Jacobs. Reprinted with the permission of Garrard Publishing Co., Champaign, Illinois.

"Mr. Rabbit and the Lovely Present" consists of the condensed text and selected illustrations from MR. RABBIT AND THE LOVELY PRESENT by Charlotte Zolotow, illustrated by Maurice Sendak. Text copyright © 1962 by Charlotte Zolotow. Pictures copyright © 1962 by Maurice Sendak. By permission of Harper & Row, Publishers, Inc. and The Bodley Head.

"The Tickle Rhyme" from TALE OF THE MONSTER HORSE by Ian Serraillier, Published by Oxford University Press. © 1950 Ian Serraillier. Reprinted by permission of the author.

"Baby Chick" from RUNNY DAYS, SUNNY DAYS by Aileen Fisher. Copyright © 1958 by Aileen Fisher. Published by Abelard-Schuman, Ltd. Reprinted by permission of the author.

"Tomorrows" from FAR AND FEW by David McCord (British title: MR. BIDERY'S SPIDERY GARDEN). Copyright © 1962 by David McCord. By permission of Little, Brown and Company and George G. Harrap & Co., Ltd.

"Bees" from RHYMES ABOUT THE COUNTRY by Marchette Chute. Copyright 1941 (Macmillan), renewal 1969 by Marchette Chute. Reprinted by permission of the author.

"Leave Herbert Alone" is adapted from LEAVE HERBERT ALONE, text © 1972 by Alma Marshak Whitney, by permission of Addison-Wesley Publishing Company, Inc.

ILLUSTRATIONS

Cover: Robert Pepper
Pages 8–13, Lyle Miller; pages 14, 15–22, Susan Lexa; pages 23–28, Carol Nicklaus; pages 29–34, Jon Goodell; pages 35–39, Judy Love; page 40, Helen Cogancherry; pages 41–48, Carol Nicklaus; pages 49–54, Frank Fretz; pages 55–60, Ronald LeHew; pages 61–68, Richard Walz; pages 69–74, Angela Adams; pages 75–80, Dora Leder; pages 81–86, Elliot Kreloff; pages 87–94, Rosekrans Hoffman; page 95, Jon McIntosh; pages 100–101, Lois Ehlert; pages 102–110, Maurice Sendak; pages 112–118, Robert Lapsley; page 119, Frank Fretz; pages 120–126, Richard Walz; pages 127–133, Judy Love; pages 134–140, Ronald Himler; page 141, Marie DeJohn; pages 142–148, Charles Robinson; pages 149–155, Richard Walz; pages 156–163, Ronald LeHew; pages 171–177, Jon R. Freidman; pages 178–185, John Wallner; pages 186–192, George Ulrich; pages 193–199, Rosekrans Hoffman; pages 200–206, Ed Parker; page 207, George Suyeoka; pages 208–214, Ronald LeHew; pages 215–222, Pam Ford.

ISBN 0-673-14807-6
Copyright © 1983, 1981,
Scott, Foresman and Company, Glenview, Illinois.
All Rights Reserved
Printed in the United States of America.

PHOTOGRAPHS

Page 96, James Robinson, *Photo Researchers, Inc.*; page 97, Virginia Carleton, *Photo Researchers, Inc.*; page 98, Syd Greenberg, *Photo Researchers, Inc.*; page 99, Mark Broulton, *Photo Researchers, Inc.*; pages 164–170, Erik Arnese.

STUDIO

Kirchoff/Wohlberg, Inc.

CONTENTS

3

SECTION ONE

A Place to Play

by Diana Heller

"Look at this place," said Lin.
"People can't play in it."

"What can we do?" said Mark.

Lin said, "We can get people to help.
We can all work together to make it
like new."

8

"I can find Bill Downs," Tom told the
boys and girls.
"Bill Downs could help."

"I can get Nan Green," said Pam.
"Nan Green could help."

"We can get all the boys and girls
to come," said Lin.

"We can work together," they all said.
"All the people can help make the park
like new."

Nan Green came.

Bill Downs came.

All the boys and girls came.

"You can help make a swing," Nan Green
told Lin.

"You can help put this slide together,"
Bill Downs told Mark and Sue.

Tom and Pam helped Bill Downs and Nan
Green make the tables.

"Now we can put the flowers in the park,"
Bill Downs said.

The boys and girls put blue flowers
under the slide.
They put yellow flowers behind the tables.
They put red flowers by the swings.
They put this in the park:

DO NOT PICK
THE FLOWERS

Now all the people come to the park.
They swing on the swings and slide down
the slide.
They work at the tables.
They look at the flowers.

The people like the new park.

Comprehension Check
1. What did the boys and girls do to make
   the park look like new?
2. What things could you do to make a
   park a good place to play?

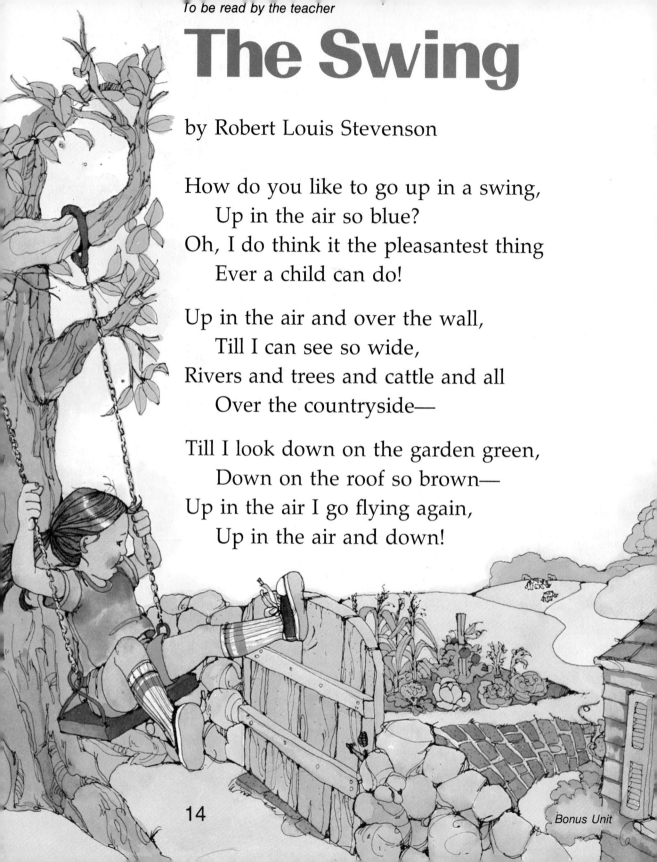

The Swing

by Robert Louis Stevenson

How do you like to go up in a swing,
  Up in the air so blue?
Oh, I do think it the pleasantest thing
  Ever a child can do!

Up in the air and over the wall,
  Till I can see so wide,
Rivers and trees and cattle and all
  Over the countryside—

Till I look down on the garden green,
  Down on the roof so brown—
Up in the air I go flying again,
  Up in the air and down!

Sam

by Timothy Loughman

Carla did not want to go out to play.

Carla said, "Lulu, we can have fun in the house.
I have a new game we can play.
You hide.
I'll look for you."

Lulu did not run away to hide.

"Hide, Lulu," Carla said.

Carla could not get Lulu to hide.

"I'll hide," Carla said.

Carla said, "Lulu, we can't
hide together."

16

"Lulu, what do you see?" said Carla.
"What are you looking at?
A bird!" said Carla.
"I'll get something to put the bird in.
I'll get a box."

"Get in," Carla said to the bird.

The bird did.

"What can we name this bird?" Carla
said to Lulu.
"We can't name it Carla.
I have that name.
We can't name it Lulu.
You have that name.
We can name the bird Sam."

18

Carla wanted Sam to sing.
But Sam would not sing.
Carla put flowers in the box.
Flowers did not make Sam sing.
Carla jumped all about.
That did not make Sam sing.
Sam would not sing at all.

Sam did not like it in the box.
Carla could see that.

"Lulu, a box is not a good place
for a bird," Carla said.
"A bird can't fly in a box.
Come on, Lulu."

"Now you can fly away," Carla
said to Sam.
And Sam did.

"Sam is flying now," said Carla.
"And Sam is singing."

Carla and Lulu could see Sam flying
far away.

"Now you and I can play," Carla said.

Lulu jumped over the table.
Carla laughed.

"You would make a good bird," Carla
said to Lulu.
"You can fly over tables.
Now all you have to do is sing."

Comprehension Check
1. What did Carla name the bird?
2. Did the bird like the box?
3. What did Carla do to make the
   bird sing?

22

Flying to the Zoo

by Diane Dzamtovski

"I wish I could fly," said Ann.
"Would you like to fly, Jake?"

"I guess I would," said Jake.

"Where could we go?" Jake asked.

Ann said, "We could go to the park.
We could go to the zoo."

He said, "I do not know.
Can I ask Teddy to come?"

Ann said, "Teddy can't come.
You and I can go," she said.
"I'll help you.
Do what I do."

"Now we are flying," she said.
"This is fun.
We made it!"

"Are we flying?" asked Jake.
Jake did not know.

24

"Where are we?" asked Jake.

"We are in the park," Ann said.
"See all the plants and the flowers?
A girl and a dog are playing.
The girl made a face at the dog.
Look at the funny face the girl made."

But Jake did not see the park
and the dog.
Jake did not see the funny face.
Jake wished he could see something.

"What do you see now?" said Jake.

Ann said, "There is the zoo."
She said, "See all the animals?"

Jake asked, "Where?
Where are the animals?"
He looked and looked for the animals.
"Is this a game?" said Jake.
Jake wished he could see what Ann
could see.

Ann said, "I see a monkey.
The monkey has on a boy's hat.
That is funny.
Do you see it, Jake?"

He said, "I do see it.
Ann, I can see the monkey."

Ann said, "You can?
Where?"

Comprehension Check

1. What did Ann see at the park?
2. What monkey did Ann see?
   What monkey did Jake see?
3. Could Ann fly? Could Jake fly?

One Day at Dave's

by Diane Dzamtovski

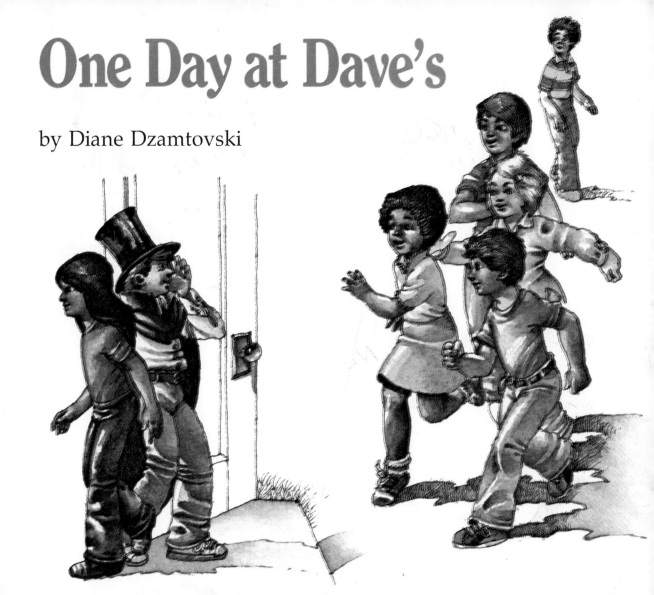

One day Dave said, "Boys and girls,
come one, come all.
I am going to do some magic."

"What are we going to see?" asked Pam.

Dave said, "You will see magic."

"Will you put some red paint in this?"
Dave said to one boy.
"And will you put some yellow paint
in?" Dave said to one girl.
"The red paint and the yellow paint
are together," Dave said.
"Now, boys and girls, what do I have?"

The boys and girls said together,
"You have orange paint."

"That is right," said Dave.
"I had red paint and I had yellow
paint.
But now I have orange paint."

"It is magic," the boys and girls said.

But one girl, Pam, said, "That is not magic.
We can all do it.
Would you like to make purple paint?
Take some red paint.
Put in some blue paint.
And what do you have?"

"Purple paint," Pete said.

"That is right," Pam said.
"You have purple paint."

Dave laughed and said, "Now you know my magic."

All the boys and girls wanted to do
the magic.

Dave took out some paper for the boys
and girls.

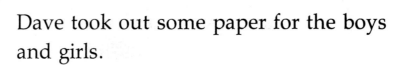

"I am going to put my name in
blue," Pete said.

"I am going to put my name in
purple," Bill said.

"I am going to make an orange box, an
orange table, and an orange dog," Pam said.

They all had fun.

Pam said, "Oh, look.
There is paper all over the place."

"And look at all the paint," Pete said.

"We have to put it away," Bill said.

Dave said, "I will do it.
This day is a magic day.
Paint and paper, go away."

"Where did it all go?" the boys and girls said.
They looked at Dave.

Dave said, "I told you I can do magic!"

Comprehension Check

1. What do you do to make purple paint?
2. Could Dave do magic?

The Magic Hat

by Timothy Loughman

"What can I do?" Betty said.
"I guess I'll play on the swing."
But she did not do that.
For she could see something behind
the swing.

"A hat," she said.
"What is a hat doing there?
And there is a book in the hat!"

Betty looked at the book's name: The
Magic Hat.

Betty did what the book said to do.
The hat did what the book said
it would!
It made flowers!

Betty said, "That will do."
And the magic hat did not make a
thing.

Bonus Unit

That day Lee came to see Betty.

"Look at this magic hat!" Betty said.

"What can it do?" Lee said.

"It makes flowers," Betty said.
"Magic hat, make flowers now."

And the hat did.

"I'll get something to put the flowers
in," Betty said.

The hat made red flowers.
The hat made yellow flowers.
The hat made purple flowers.

Lee did not know what to do.
"Magic hat, do not make flowers,"
she said.
But that did not help.

"Hold it, magic hat," she said.
But that did not help.

"Hat, do not do that."
The hat would not do what Lee told it
to do.

38

Betty came in.
"What is going on?" Betty said.
"That will do, magic hat."

"It is a good thing you came in,"
Lee said.
"What will we do with all the flowers?"

"People like flowers," Betty said.
"We will see that people get flowers."

And they did.

Comprehension Check
1. How did Betty know what to do to get the magic hat to make flowers?
2. What would you like a magic hat to make?

My Uncle's Garden

by Kay Douglas

My uncle has a garden
with lilies
and with roses.

My uncle has a garden
that is beautiful
to see.

Still, I wish my uncle's garden
had dandelions
in it,

For dandelions' golden heads
are beautiful
to me.

The Last Bag of Peanuts

by Janet Gopin

"Can we see more animals?" asked Lee.

"You wanted to see the monkeys,"
Ann said.
"We did.
You wanted to see the seals.
We did.
Now I want to sit down and
have the peanuts."

Ann said, "Maria, get out the peanuts."

Maria got out the bags of peanuts.
She said, "One, two, three, four, five,
six, seven, eight.
There are eight bags of peanuts."

Maria gave a bag of peanuts to Ann.
"Now there are seven bags of peanuts,"
she said.

"Seven bags?" Hector said.
"I want one."

42

Maria gave a bag of peanuts to Hector.

"Now there are six bags," she said.

She gave out three more bags.
Lee got a bag of peanuts.
Tom got a bag of peanuts.
Doris got a bag of peanuts.

"I gave out five bags," Maria said.
"I have three.
Five and three are eight."

"I do not have one," said Kim.

"Have a bag of peanuts," Maria said.
"Now there are two."

Tom said, "There are two more
bags of peanuts."

Maria said, "But I get one bag.
Now there is one more bag of peanuts."

44

"I want it," said Lee.

Doris said, "You have one.
And I like peanuts more than you do."

"Your bag of peanuts has four more
peanuts than my bag," Kim said
to Maria.

"You have six peanuts more than I have,"
Hector said to Tom.

"You have four peanuts more than I have,"
Doris said to Lee.

"Ann, who gets the last bag of peanuts?" asked Lee.

Ann said, "We can play a game to see who gets it."

"What is the game?" asked Hector.

Ann said, "I'll put down the name of an animal.
Guess the animal and you will get the last bag of peanuts."

46

Hector asked, "Is it a bird?"

Ann said, "It is not a bird."

"Is it a dog?" Lee asked.

Ann said, "It is not a dog."

"Is it an elephant?" Kim asked.

Ann said, "It is not an elephant."

Tom said, "Look, it *is* an elephant."

"Now we know who gets the last bag of peanuts," they all said.

Comprehension Check
1. Who got the last bag of peanuts?
2. Can you name five animals you could see at the zoo?

Growing Plants

by Peter Martin Wortmann

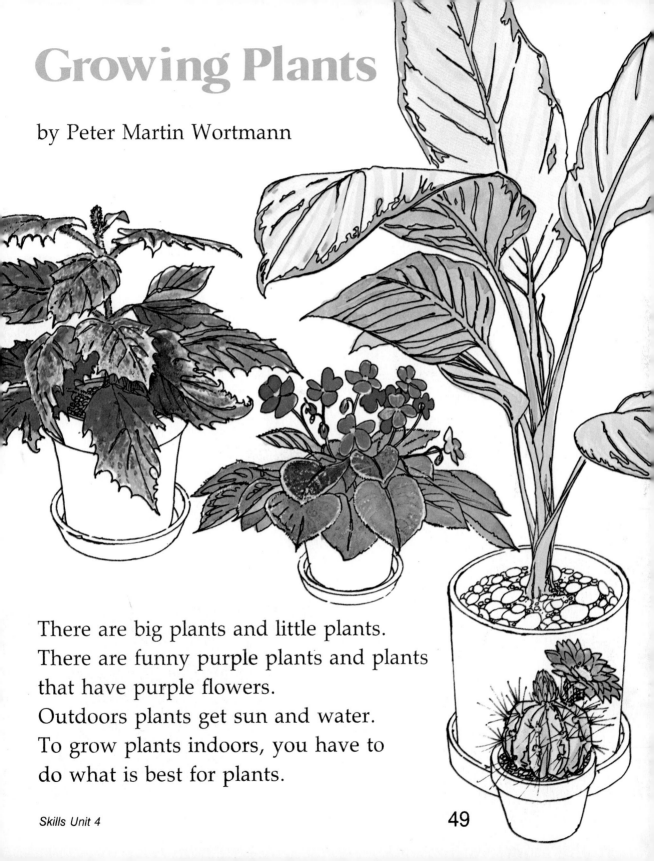

There are big plants and little plants.
There are funny purple plants and plants
that have purple flowers.
Outdoors plants get sun and water.
To grow plants indoors, you have to
do what is best for plants.

You will have to pick the best place
for your plants to grow.
You will find that some places are better
for some plants than for others.

50

All plants need water and light.
Some plants need all the light they can get.
These plants can go with no water for days.
A little water is better than too much water for these plants.
It is best for these plants to face the sun all day.

Some plants grow yellow if they are
in the sun all day.
No sun at all is better than too much
sun for these plants.
A little light is what these plants like
best.
They like water too.
Water helps plants like these grow big
and green.

52

There are some plants that grow flowers.
Plants that grow flowers need much more
light than plants that are all green.
If they get too little light, some of the
flowers will not grow.
If they get the water and sun that they
need, flowers will grow.

Some people like to sing to the plants they have.

No one knows if this helps the plants grow.

What we do know is that all plants need water and light.

And the more you know about what your plants need, the better your plants will grow.

Comprehension Check
1. What do plants need to grow?
2. What is the best place to put plants that grow flowers?
3. What plants do you like best?

54

The Big Sweep

by Bobbi Katz

Do you know how much work
our class can do?
Our class can do more
than a dog like you!

Our class can sweep out
the places I name.
A big place—a little place—
to us it's the same.

We can sweep out a house.
We can sweep out a zoo.
There is not one thing
that our class can't do!

We can sweep out a box.
We can sweep out a hat.
We can sweep out a bag.
Our class can do that.

We can sweep the park.
We can sweep the swings.
We can keep up and sweep up
all places and things!

We can sweep out the cold.
We can sweep on the light.
We can sweep it up best.
We can sweep it up right.

How can we do it?
Sweep things all day?
There isn't much to it.
We make work like play.

If you gave us a goat,
we could sweep the goat's coat.
If you gave us a game,
we would sweep all the same.

58

How much can we do?
Do you want to know?
If you gave us the work,
we would get up and go.

We could sweep the sun yellow.
We would sweep water blue.
If you want purple flowers,
we could do that for you.

We are the best class
at this sweeping game.
Our class is the best class
that you could name!

Comprehension Check

1. What things *could* the class sweep out?
   Could your class sweep out the same
   things?
2. What can your class do best?

The Three Wishes

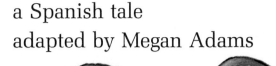

a Spanish tale
adapted by Megan Adams

"I wish I had a big dog," said Bill.

"I wish I had a big boat," said Sue.

"I wish we had a big house," said Father.

"There are people who wish for something and they get it," said Bill.

Then a bird came.
It had on a little blue coat.
It had on a little yellow hat.

The bird said, "You can have three wishes."

"Who said that?" asked Bill.

"I did," said the bird.
"All you have to do is wish for something," the bird said.
"Then you can have it.
You have three wishes."
And the little bird left.

They did not know what to wish for first.
"How about wishing for a dog first?"
Bill asked.

"No, a big dog would jump all over the new house," said Father.

"What new house?" asked Sue.

"The new house we are going to wish for first," Father said.

"But I want to wish for a big boat," said Sue.

"A big dog is a better wish," said Bill.

"A boat!" said Sue.

"A dog!" said Bill.

"Oh," Sue said to Bill, "I wish you would fly away."

And Bill did!
Bill was flying.
Bill was flying away.

"Help," said Bill.

"Oh, no!" said Father. "Bill, come down."

"Oh, no!" Sue said. "Look what I did.
I wish Bill would come down."

And Bill did.

"That was not a good thing to wish for,"
Bill said to Sue.

"I know," said Sue.
"That is the last wish I will make."

66

And then the bird came.
"What do you want for your last wish?"
the bird asked.

Father said, "Not a thing.
We have all we want."

Sue said, "And we like what we have!"

Bill said, "Now we have one more wish
to make.
And we all have the same wish:
Go away!"

And the little bird did.

Comprehension Check

1. What did Sue, Bill, and Father want to wish for?
2. What made Bill wish that the bird would go away?

The Thing

by Peter Martin Wortmann

"What a day!" said Carmen.
"What can we do on a day like this?"

"Pam will have a good thing to do.
Ask Pam," said Ray.

Carmen asked Pam.

"We can make The Thing," said Pam.

"The Thing?
What is The Thing?" Carmen and
Ray asked together.

Pam said, "The Thing is what you want it to be.
All you have to do is make one.
The first thing it has to have is a body.
Cut out a body for your Thing."

"What is a Thing's body like?" asked Carmen.

Pam said, "Make a body for your Thing.
And you will see what a Thing's body looks like."

Pam said, "Now your Thing has to have
feet."

"How many feet can a Thing have?"
asked Ray.

Pam said, "Things can have many feet.
You could make a Thing with three legs
and six feet.
You could make a Thing with four legs
and eight feet."

Pam said, "Your Thing looks good with feet and legs.
Now you can work on the arms and hands.
Cut out your Thing's arms and hands."

"Can a Thing have four hands?" asked Ray.

Pam said, "A Thing can have all the hands that you want it to have.
Four hands will look good.
Six hands would look better."

"Now all your Thing has to have is
a head," Pam said.
"Cut out a head for your Thing."

"Can a Thing have a little head?"
asked Ray.

"Can I make a Thing with three big
noses?" asked Carmen.

Pam said, "A Thing is what you
want it to be.
Your Thing can have five noses.
It can have six noses.
It can have seven noses!"

Pam said, "Now all you have got to do is
put your Thing together and paint it.
Paint the legs orange and blue.
Paint the head purple.
Paint it how you want it.
That is what a Thing is all about,"
she said.

Comprehension Check

1. What is the first thing you do to
   make a Thing?
2. How many hands can a Thing have?
3. What is the last thing you have
   to do to make a Thing?

A PLACE FOR KIP

by Marjorie Slavick Frank

There was a boy named Pete.
There was a dog named Kip.
Pete and Kip played together all
the time.

One day a big box came to the house.
The box was for Pete.
Grandfather had told Pete about it.
Pete looked to see what was in
the box.

Pete said, "It's a new bike.
What a good time you and I can have
with this bike, Kip.
Come on.
I'll give you a ride."

Pete jumped on his bike.
Then he looked at Kip.
Kip did not jump.
There was no place for her on the bike.
Pete could not give her a ride.

"I can't give you a ride," Pete said.
"But I'll go for a little ride.
Then we will play together."

Pete's ride that day was not little
at all.
It lasted all day.
He liked his new bike.

Pete took his bike out the next day
and the next day and the next day.
He did not have time to play with
Kip now.
She was sad.

Kip wanted Pete to play with her and
not ride his bike.
She wanted to go places with Pete and
have a good time too.
Where was he?
She would have to look for Pete.

Kip looked for Pete.
She looked all over.
She could not find Pete.
Kip was sad.
She was too sad to keep looking.
She sat down!

Then Pete came.
There was Pete!
Pete said, "Kip, look at my bike."

Kip picked up her head and looked at
Pete's bike.

There was something new on the bike.
What was it for?
Kip did not know.
Pete would have to help her find out.

Comprehension Check

1. What made Kip sad?
2. What did Pete put on his bike?
3. What was the box for?

A City of People

by W. Martin Young

Some people say that all the city has
is big buildings.
But there is something that they don't
know.
The city has more than big buildings.
The city has people.
The city has many people.

It is the start of the day.
Doors swing open and people come out.
Some people walk to work.
Some people like to ride bikes to
work.
Some people drive to work.

There are people who help you get to work.
They say, "Walk."
They say, "Don't walk."
They know what to do.
If you keep your eyes open, you will know
what to do too.

There is work here in the city.

☆ And there are many people here to do the work.

☆ But there is some time to walk about and talk.

There are many people to talk to.

☆ There are many things to see and do for fun too.

84

Some of the people in this city have dogs.
You can see the people walk the dogs at
the start and end of the day.
The dogs start to run in the park.
Some of the people don't like to run.
Then it looks like the dogs are walking
the people.

Open your eyes and look about.
You will start to see all the people
that make this city a good place.
They don't have all the birds and flowers
here that you see in some places.
But they do have people here to
walk and talk and play with.

Comprehension Check

1. What do some people say about the city?
2. What two things do you like best about the city?
3. What two things don't you like about the city?

TALK

an African tale
adapted by Rebecca Haber

One time, a man was in his garden
picking flowers.

One of the flowers said, "You are
here at last.
You did not water me.
But now you have come to pick me.
Go away!"

"Who said that?" the man said.
The man picked up his head and looked
at his goat.
"Did you say something?" he asked.

"The goat did not talk to you," the
man's dog said.
"It was the flower.
The flower told you to go away."

The man began to run to the mayor.

"Where are you going?" a woman asked.

The man said, "My flower talked.
My dog talked too."

"Is that all?" the woman asked.

"Did you do what the flower told you
to do?" the woman's table asked.

"A talking table!" the woman said.

She began to run.
The man began to run too.

"Where are you going?" a boy with a
bike asked.

"My flower talked," the man said.

"And my table talked!" the woman said.

"Is that all?" asked the boy.

The boy's bike said, "You would run too."

"A talking bike!" the boy said.

He began to run.
The man and the woman began to run too.
They looked for the mayor.
The mayor opened the door and came out.
She sat down on a chair.

92

The man said, "My flower talked.
My dog talked too."

"And my table," said the woman.

"And my bike," said the boy.

At last the mayor said, "Flowers
do not talk.
Tables and bikes do not talk.
This all makes me laugh.
You all have work to do.
Now go and do it."

They left.

The mayor sat on the chair.

"How about that?" the chair said.

"Who said that?" asked the mayor.

Comprehension Check

1. What did the flower say to the
   man?
2. Who did the man, the woman, and
   the boy run to see?
3. What would you do if a table
   talked to you?

The Tickle Rhyme

by Ian Serraillier

"Who's that tickling my back?"
said the wall.
"Me," said a small Caterpillar.
"I'm learning to crawl."

Spiders and Webs

by Mark Adams

What do you know about spiders?
Did you know that spiders have
eight legs?
Spiders have eight eyes too.

Spiders live in all kinds of places.
Some kinds of spiders live in parks.
Some kinds of spiders live in houses.
There is one kind of spider that lives
in water.

Spiders do not have to be told how
to make webs.
They know how to do it.
Not all webs look the same.
Some webs are big.
Some webs are little.
All spider webs do the same thing.
They help the spiders get food.

You can make a spider web too.
Here is what you will need.
You will need paper.
You will need something to cut with.
You will need something to
draw lines with.

To start, fold the
paper two times.

1   fold

2   fold

fold

Next draw lines
on the paper.
Draw the lines to
look like these lines.

Now cut on the lines
you made.
Cut on the lines,
but don't cut on the folds.
The paper will
look like this.

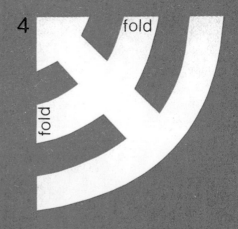

3   fold

fold

4   fold

fold

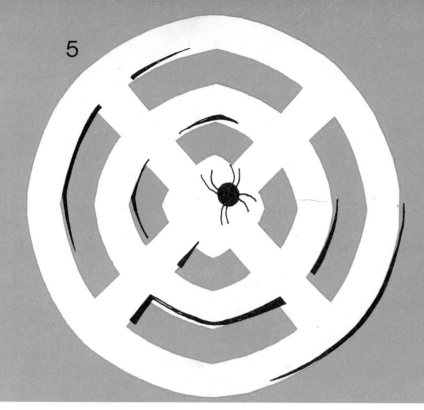

5

Now open the paper.
Open it and you will see a spider web.
But you need a spider too.
What kind of spider will you draw?
Draw one.
Draw eight legs on your spider.
Then put the spider on the web.

Comprehension Check

1. Where do spiders live?
2. What are spider webs for?
3. Do you like spiders?

Mr. Rabbit and the Lovely Present

by Charlotte Zolotow
pictures by Maurice Sendak

"Mr. Rabbit," said the little girl,
"I want help."

"Help, little girl, I'll give you help
if I can," said Mr. Rabbit.

"Mr. Rabbit," said the little girl,
"it's about my mother."

"Your mother?" said Mr. Rabbit.

"It's her birthday," said the little girl.

"Happy birthday to her then," said
Mr. Rabbit.
"What are you giving her?"

"That's just it," said the little girl.
"I have nothing to give her."

"Nothing to give your mother on her
birthday?" said Mr. Rabbit.
"Little girl, you really do want help."

"I would like to give her something
that she likes," said the little girl.
"But what?"

"Yes, what?" said Mr. Rabbit.

"She likes red," said the little girl.

"Red," said Mr. Rabbit.
"You can't give her red."

"Something red, maybe," said the little girl.

"Oh, something red," said Mr. Rabbit.

"What is red?" said the little girl.

"There are red roofs," said Mr. Rabbit.

"No, we have a roof," said the little girl.
"I don't want to give her that."

"There are red birds," said Mr. Rabbit.

"No," said the little girl, "she likes
birds in trees."

"There are red fire engines," said Mr. Rabbit.

"No," said the little girl, "she doesn't
like fire engines."

"Well," said Mr. Rabbit, "there are apples."

"Good," said the little girl.
"She likes apples.
But I need something else."

"What else does she like?" said Mr. Rabbit.

"Well, she likes yellow," said the
little girl.

"Yellow," said Mr. Rabbit.
"You can't give her yellow."

"Something yellow, maybe," said the
little girl.

"Oh, something yellow," said Mr. Rabbit.

"What is yellow?" said the little girl.

"The sun is yellow," said Mr. Rabbit.

"But I can't give her the sun," said the
little girl, "though I would if I could."

"A canary bird is yellow," said Mr. Rabbit.

"She likes birds in trees," the little
girl said.

"That's right, you told me," said Mr. Rabbit.
"Bananas are yellow."

"Oh, good," said the little girl.
"She likes bananas.
I need something else though."

"What else does she like?" said Mr. Rabbit.

"She likes blue," the little girl said.

"Blue. You can't give her blue," said
Mr. Rabbit.

"Something blue, maybe," said the little girl.

"Lakes are blue," said the rabbit.

"But I can't give her a lake, you know,"
said the little girl.

"Stars are blue," said Mr. Rabbit.

"I can't give her stars," the little girl said,
"but I would if I could."

"Bluebirds are blue, but she likes
birds in trees," said Mr. Rabbit.

"Right," said the little girl.

108

"How about blue grapes?" said Mr. Rabbit.

"Yes," said the little girl.
"That is good, very good.
She likes grapes.
Now I have apples and bananas and grapes."

"That makes a good gift," said Mr. Rabbit.
"All you need now is a basket."

"I have a basket," said the little girl.
So she took her basket, and she filled
it with the yellow bananas and the red
apples and the blue grapes.
It made a lovely present.

"Thank you for your help, Mr. Rabbit,"
said the little girl.

"Not at all," said Mr. Rabbit.
"Very glad to help."

"Good-by, now," said the little girl.

"Good-by," said Mr. Rabbit, "and a
happy birthday and a happy basket of
fruit to your mother."

110

SECTION TWO

The First Bluebird

a Native American tale
adapted by Rebecca Haber

At one time all birds and animals had
the same color.
But one bird, Jimmy-er-ye, was not
happy.

One day he looked at the sky.
He said, "The sky is pretty.
Oh, I wish I could be the color of
the sky!"

112

A Cloud said, "Oh, little bird!
Would you like to be pretty like the
sky?"

"I would like to be pretty like the
sky," said the bird.

The Cloud said, "Then do this for
four days.
Go in the water.
Then fly and sing:
'I am happy.
I am going to be like the sky.'"

Jimmy-er-ye said, "Oh, I will then
be blue like the sky."

114

The next day, Jimmy-er-ye did what
the Cloud had said to do.
He came out of the water.
He said, "I am happy.
I am going to be like the sky."

But Jimmy-er-ye looked the same.
He was not blue.
He was not happy.
Jimmy-er-ye was sad.

The next day, and the next day, he
did the same thing.
But he looked the same.
Jimmy-er-ye was not blue.

On the last day the Cloud said one
more time, "Would you like to be blue
like the sky?"

"I would," said the bird.

The Cloud said, "Go in the water one
more time.
Then fly and sing:
'The sky is blue.
I am blue too.'"

Jimmy-er-ye came out of the water.
Then he saw that he was blue.
He was happy.

He said, "The Cloud has made me
pretty like the sky."

And the Cloud was happy she had made
Jimmy-er-ye the first bluebird.

Comprehension Check
1. What made Jimmy-er-ye want to be
   the color of the sky?
2. Who helped Jimmy-er-ye to be blue?

Baby Chick

by Aileen Fisher

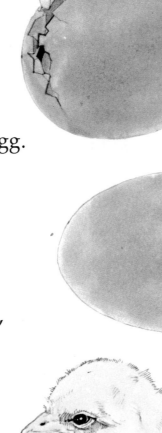

Peck
   Peck
      Peck
on the warm brown egg.
OUT comes a neck.
OUT comes a leg.
How
   does
      a chick,
who's not been about,
discover the trick
of how to get out?

Grandfather's Secret

by Lisa Eisenberg

One day Sue and Tom walked to
Grandfather's house.

"I have something for you two to do,"
Grandfather said.
He got up out of the armchair.

"Is it a game?" asked Sue.

"It's a secret," said Grandfather.

Sue and Tom walked with Grandfather
out of the house to the garden.
Grandfather took something out of his
coat.

"What is that?" Tom asked.

"It's a secret seed," Grandfather said.
"Plant it for me.
After it grows, you will see what it
is."

Tom and Sue planted the seed.
Grandfather took out some more seeds.
Sue and Tom planted seeds all day.
At the end of the day, Grandfather had
not said what the seeds would be.

All Grandfather would say was, "After
the seeds grow, you will know.
Soon the seeds will grow."

Sue and Tom walked home.
"Someday soon we will find out what
we planted," Tom said.

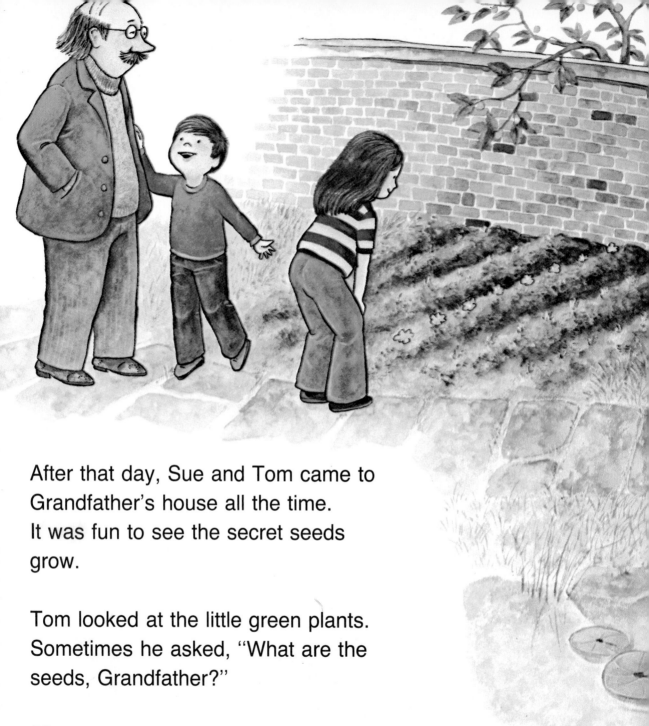

After that day, Sue and Tom came to
Grandfather's house all the time.
It was fun to see the secret seeds
grow.

Tom looked at the little green plants.
Sometimes he asked, "What are the
seeds, Grandfather?"

"Soon you will know, Tom," said
Grandfather.

One day Grandfather said, "Your mother
told me that you are going to
Greenwater Park for eight days.
After eight days, it will be time to see
what the seeds are."

Mother, Father, Sue, and Tom had a
good time at Greenwater Park.
After eight days, they came home.
Sue and Tom ran to Grandfather's house.

124

Tom said, "Grandfather, we are here!
We came to see the secret seeds."

Sue and Tom ran out of the house to
the garden to see the plants.
They saw the plants.
They saw a rabbit too!
It took a bite out of one of the
plants and ran away.

Grandfather laughed.
"That rabbit knows my secret," he said.

Sue and Tom laughed too.
"It knows we planted a salad," Sue said.

"And it left some for you and me too,"
said Tom.

And that night Grandfather, Mother, Father,
Sue, and Tom had a big green salad.

Comprehension Check
1. What was Grandfather's secret?
2. What kinds of plants would you
   like to grow?

126

Something About Kites

by Janet Gopin

"Jim, Pete is here," Jim's mother said.

Pete said, "Look at this pretty green
kite I have.
Do you want to come with me and fly
it in the park?"

"That would be great," said Jim.
"Mother, can I go to the park?"

"You can go," said Mother.

"Pam, Jim is going to the park,"
Mother said.
"Would you like to go with Jim?"

"Great," said Pam.
She put down the book that she was
reading.

"That is a pretty kite you have,
Pete," said Pam.
"I know something about kites."

"You are too little to know about
kites," said Jim.

Jim said to Pam, "You go play.
Pete and I are going to fly the kite."

"Can't I fly the kite with you?"
asked Pam.

"No," said Jim.

Pete took the kite.
He started to run with it.
The kite would not fly.

"The kite is too big," said Jim.
"If we had a little kite, it would fly."

"No, this kite is not new," said Pete.
"If we had a new kite, it would fly."

"I know how to make it fly," said Pam.

Skills Unit 11

"You are too little to know about
kites," said Pete.
"I will make it fly.
I will run as fast as I can."

He ran to the left.
He ran to the right.
He ran as fast as he could.
The kite would not fly.

"I can make it fly," said Pam.
"I know a little secret about kites."

"If *we* can't make this kite fly, no
one can," said Jim.

"I can," said Pam.
"Here, hold this side."

"What are you doing?" said Pete.

"What is the secret?" said Jim.

Pam laughed and said, "It is not a secret.
It is a kite tail.
This kite will fly if it has a tail."

Then Jim took the right side of the kite.
Pete took the left side.
Pam took the tail.

They started to run.
The kite started to fly.
It looked pretty flying over
the park.

"What a great kite!" Jim said.
"Pam, you do know about kites."

Comprehension Check

1. What did Pam do to make the kite
   fly?
2. How did Pam know what to do?
3. If you wanted to make a kite, what
   would you need?

Bonus Unit

Santa Fe Festival

by Gary Korn

The Santa Fe Festival is here!
People come from all over.
Some people fly to the festival.
Some people drive.
Some people ride horses and bikes.
And some people, like me, walk to the festival.
The festival will last for two days.
There is much to see and do.
No one will want the festival to end.

My mother, father, and I walk to the
festival park.
There are many people there.
I can't guess how many.
There are people who made things for
the festival.
And there are people, like us, who have
come to see all the handmade things.

There are handmade bags, coats, and kites.
There are pretty paintings of people and animals.
If it can be made by hand, you will see it at the festival.

136

I see a little handmade boat.
I like this boat.
I ask the man if he made it.
The man made the boat.
He worked on it for three days.
My mother and father say I can have
the boat.
I am happy!

The people who hold the festival give
prizes away.
They will give prizes for the best of
the handmade things.
I wish the boat the man made would get
a prize.

138   *Bonus Unit*

Next we go to see the people dance.
The people get in a line.
One man starts to dance.
The others dance with him.
The dance looks like fun.
I start to dance too.

Now it is time to go.
My mother, father, and I start walking
to the house.
I wish tomorrow would come soon.
Then I can go to the festival one more
time.

Comprehension Check

1. What are some of the things people
   can see and do at the festival?
2. What makes the girl wish
   tomorrow would come soon?

Tomorrows

by David McCord

Tomorrows never seem to stay,
Tomorrows will be yesterday
Before you know.
Tomorrows have a sorry way
Of turning into just today,
And so . . . and so . . .

BIG RED

by James Tobin

Today was Mark's first day at camp.
But Mark did not like camp.
He did not like the games that the
boys and girls played.
He did not like the funny purple hat
he had to put on.
Mark did not like one thing about camp.

"Hi, Mark. I am Bob," said a big man with
a purple hat.
"How do you like camp?"

"I don't," Mark said.
"I want to go home today."

"I would like to take you to see
something first," Bob said.
"I will take you to see a pretty
red horse.
Come with me."

Mark walked with Bob.

Bob got up on the horse.
"Would you like to take a ride?"

"Thank you, I would," Mark called out.

"Here, I will pull you up," said Bob.
Bob pulled Mark up on the horse.

144

The horse ran fast.
"Go, Big Red. Go!" Bob called out to
the horse.

"Go, Big Red. Go!" Mark said.
Big Red ran and ran.

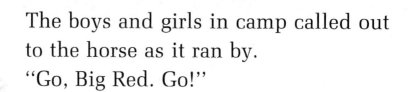

The boys and girls in camp called out
to the horse as it ran by.
"Go, Big Red. Go!"

Mark was laughing.
"Go, Big Red. Go!" Mark called out.

A ride on Big Red was better than a
ride on a slide.
It was better than a ride on a bike.

146

"Walk now, Big Red," Bob said to the
horse.
Big Red pulled up its head and
started to walk.

The boys and girls helped Mark get down.

"Was the ride fun?" one girl asked Mark.

"It was," Mark said.
"Thank you, Big Red," Mark said to
the horse.
"Thank you," Mark said to Bob.

"Do you want me to take you home
today?" Bob asked.
"I will call your mother and father."

"No, thank you, Bob.
Camp is great!"
Mark ran away to play with the boys
and girls.

Comprehension Check

1. What did Mark not like about camp
   at first?
2. What made Bob take Mark on a ride
   on Big Red?
3. What animals do you like?

The Picnic

by Megan McCarthy Scarpa

Nan and her father came over to my
house today.
They came on bikes.

Nan said to me, "Get something to eat
and drink.
Get out your bike.
We are going on a picnic!"

I said, "First I want to ask Carla to come too."

And we ran all the way to Carla's house.

"Do you want to come on our picnic today?" Nan asked.

Carla said, "Thank you. That would be fun."

150

So Carla got something to eat and drink.
She put these things in a paper bag.
Then she pulled out her bike.
We walked to my house to get Nan's father.

On the way I said, "What a great day
for a picnic!"

At my house, Nan's father was talking to my mother and father.

I got something to eat and drink.

"Can you eat and drink all that?" asked Carla.

"I can," I said, so I put it all in a paper bag.
Then we all put on our coats.
I got my bike.

Carla looked outdoors first.
She said, "Oh, no.
Look outside."

I looked out, but I did not like what I
saw.
It was raining.

"How can we have a picnic now?" Carla
asked.

"We can't go outside," Nan said.

"A picnic in the rain is not any fun!"
I said.

We all sat down and looked at our bags
of food.

Then my mother said, "I know a way you
can have the picnic.
You can have the picnic indoors."

154

So that is the way we did it!

We had an indoor picnic.

We took out what we had to eat and drink.

It was so good.

There was no food left.

After that we played games.

We had fun.

Carla said that we could ask her to an indoor picnic any time!

Comprehension Check

1. What kind of picnic did they have?
2. Is an indoor picnic better than an outdoor one?

Bonus Unit

The Turtle Who Talked Too Much

a Jataka tale adapted by Arthur Yorinks

There was a turtle who talked too much.

"Walking is fun," the turtle said.
"Eating and drinking are fun.
But talking is the best kind of fun."

He would talk to anyone.

"Good day, Spider," the turtle said.
"How is your web?"

The turtle talked and talked and talked.
There was no end to it.

The turtle's grandfather said, "Turtle,
stop talking so much.
You would do better to find food for the
cold days."

The turtle did not want to find food.

"Thank you, but talking is more fun than
anything," he said.

One day two birds came by.

"We are going to fly someplace warm,"
they said.
"Would you like to come?"

"But I can't fly," the turtle said.

"You can come with us," said the
birds.

"What do I have to do?" asked the turtle.

"First go find a stick," one bird said.

So the turtle got a stick.

"What are you doing with that stick?"
asked his grandfather.

"I am going to fly," said the turtle.

"What kind of way is that to talk?"
asked Grandfather.
"You are a turtle.
You can't fly."

"I can," said the turtle.
"We will fly far away."

160

The turtle went to the birds with his stick.

"Now bite on the stick," the birds said. "And don't talk!"

"I will not say a thing," the turtle said. And he went to bite the stick.

One bird took the right end of the stick. The other bird took the left end of the stick.

"Here we go," said the birds.

Up and up they went.
The birds went flying up with the
turtle holding onto the stick.
He could see houses and people.
He could see water.
It was so much fun.
The turtle had to say something.

162

So he began to talk.
And down he went, right in the water.
The birds went on flying.

"I guess I talk too much," the turtle
said.
And from that day on, the turtle did not
go anywhere at all.

Comprehension Check

1. What did the turtle like to do best?
2. What made the turtle fly?

Fire and Smoke

by Wendy Ableman

The little dog did not have a home.
Day after day he walked here and there.
He walked all over looking for a home.
One night he walked to a new place.

There were big houses there.
But the dog saw that things were not
right.

There was too much smoke.
The dog saw that a house was on fire!

164

The dog got into the house.
He jumped on the people.
He pulled at the people.
Now the people could see the fire too.
They called the firefighters to come
and help.
The firefighters came fast, and soon
the fire was out.

After the fire the people were talking
to a firefighter.
They said, "We did not know there was
a fire.
We would not have called for help.
This dog saw the fire."

The firefighter asked, "Is he your dog?"

"No," the people said.

Skills Unit 14

The firefighter looked at the dog and
said, "Good work, boy.
What a dog!
If you don't have a home, you can come
to live at the firehouse.
You will make a good fire dog.
We will call you Smoke."

Now the firehouse is Smoke's home.
The firefighters are kind to Smoke.
They give him food.
When there are no fires, they run and
play with Smoke.
The firefighters and Smoke have a good
time together.

168

Smoke and the firefighters go to
calls for help.
He rides behind the firefighters.
Smoke is a big help.
He has a good nose for a fire.
Sometimes Smoke's nose finds the fire
first.

"Good boy," say the firefighters.
"You saw the fire.
Now we can see the fire too."

People sometimes say, "Where there is smoke, you will find fire."
But the firefighters say, "Where there is fire, you will find Smoke."

Comprehension Check
1. What did the dog do when he saw that the house was on fire?
2. Is Smoke a good name for the dog?
3. What are some things you can do if you see a house on fire?

170

Would You Like to Be a Fox?

by Ali Reich

Would you like to be a fox for a day?
You could find out what a fox is like.
You could find out all those things
that foxes know.
You could do all those things that
foxes do.

Do you know what a fox is like?
A fox isn't too big.
A fox isn't too small.
A fox can run fast.

172

Do you know what a fox's house is like?
A fox's house is not out in the open.
The fox's home is in a secret place.
The fox can see out and no one can see in.
There are two openings in the fox's house.
If something stops the fox from going out one opening, it can go out the other.

A fox sleeps in the daytime.
At night it looks for food.
A mother and father fox work
to help the little foxes grow.

Little foxes can't see at first.
The mother feeds the little foxes.
The father gets the mother many
small animals to eat.

174

At last the yellow eyes of the little
foxes open.
But the little foxes need a mother and
father for many days to come.
The mother fox and father fox don't
stop helping the little ones.

They wash the little foxes.
They give food to the little foxes.
They stop and play with the little
foxes.

One night the mother and father fox
take the little foxes out for a walk.
The big foxes look out for the small
ones.
The mother fox and the father fox will
stop the little foxes if they go too
far away.

Soon the little foxes will need to
know how to find food.
But there will be time for those
things.
Now they want to stop and play.

Comprehension Check
1. What is a fox's house like?
2. How do the mother fox and father
   fox help the little foxes?
3. What animal would you like to be?

The Wind and the Sun

a fable by Aesop
adapted by Regina Neuman

One day the Sun and the Wind looked down.
They saw flowers opening and birds flying.
They saw dogs playing and people laughing.

"What a good day we have made," said the Sun.

The Wind said, "We? How have you helped to make this a good day?
I am the Wind.
I can do more than you."

178

"Look at all the things I can do,"
the Wind said.
Then the Wind blew.

Hats came off.
Flowers blew away.
Papers of all kinds went flying.

"There!" the Wind said to the Sun.
"Can you do that?"

"No, I can't," the Sun said.
"I am the Sun, not the Wind.
But I can do things too."

The Wind laughed and laughed.
"We will soon find out what you can
do."
Then the Wind said, "Look down.
There is a little girl playing in the
park.
Can you make her take off her green
coat?
I can.
Look and see."

180

One more time the Wind blew.
It blew and blew.

Papers of all kinds went flying.
Flowers blew away.
Hats came off.
But the green coat did not.

The more the Wind blew, the more the little girl needed her coat to keep warm.
The Wind could not make her take it off.
At last the Wind gave up.

"Now you will see," said the Sun.
"I will do what you could not do."

Then the Sun looked down on the little
girl and laughed in a kind, warm way.

"How warm the sun is," the little girl
said.
"I am warm all over now.
I don't need my coat at all."

And with that the little girl took off
her green coat.
She put it down and went on playing.

184

"There," the Sun said.
"I did what you could not do."

Comprehension Check

1. What made the little girl keep her
   coat on as the Wind blew?
2. How did the Sun get the little
   girl to take off her coat?
3. Can the Wind and the Sun talk?
   What can the Wind and the Sun do?

Lost and Found

by Pearl Wolf

Today Mr. Best, Mrs. Best, and Mark are going to buy Mark a new coat.

"Will you buy me a green coat?" asked Mark.

"We will buy you a nice coat," said Mrs. Best.

"Green is nice," said Mark.

"Do you need any help?" asked Mr. Park.

"Yes, thank you.
Where are coats for boys?" asked Mr. Best.

"Coats can be found over there," said Mr. Park.

186

Mr. Best said, "Here is a nice red coat."

"Here's a nice blue coat," said Mrs. Best.

"Take your coat off and put these two coats on," said Mr. Best.

"The red coat is much too big," said Mr. Best.

"The blue coat is much too small," said Mrs. Best.

"That's good," said Mark. "I want a green coat."

"We will look some more," said Mrs.
Best.
Mrs. Best looked for a coat for Mark.
Mr. Best looked too.
But Mark did not look.
Mark saw some pretty lights.
The lights went on and off.
He went to see what they were.

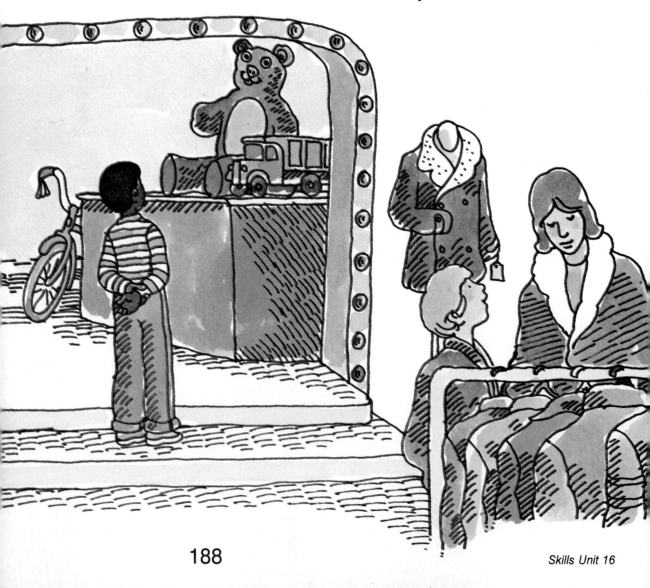

188

"I cannot find Mark," Mr. Best said.

"Which coat will you buy?" Mr. Park asked.

"Mark is lost!" Mrs. Best said.

"We found two coats, but we lost Mark!"
Mr. Best said.

"Which way did he go?" asked Mr. Park.

"We don't know which way he went," said
Mrs. Best.

Mr. Best looked under all the coats.
"He is not under the coats," said Mr.
Best.

They looked up and down the shop.

Then Mrs. Best said, "I found him!
He is over there looking at those lights."

190

"We looked all over for you," said Mr.
Best.

"We could not find you," said Mrs. Best.

"But I was here all the time!" said Mark.
"Did you buy me two green coats?" Mark
asked.

They all laughed.

Mrs. Best said, "Try these coats on.
See which one you like better.
Then we will buy you a green coat."

Comprehension Check

1. What color coat did Mark want?
2. Where was Mark?
   What was he doing?
3. What would you do if you were lost?

You Must Never Look Under the Bed

by Marjorie Slavick Frank

LEONARD: Mother and Pam, I have lost
my new book.
Did you see it, Grandmother?
Where could I look?

PAM: Look under those flowers
   Which grow in the box.
   Look under the birdhouse.
   Look under the rocks.

LEONARD: Flowers and rocks
   Are not places to look,
   When what you are looking for
   Looks like a book.
   I must look in the place
   Where the book was last read.
   Oh! Now I know where.
   I'll look under the bed!

194

GRANDMOTHER: Look under the bed?
Is that what you said?
You must never, no, never
Look under the bed!

MOTHER: Look indoors. Look outdoors.
Look there for your book.

LEONARD: I was reading in bed.
That's where I must look.

GRANDMOTHER: Sit down, Leonard.
Keep this in your head.
You must never, no, never
Look under the bed!

GRANDMOTHER: You can swing on a vine.
You can slide on a line.
You can look for and jump for
All things of all kinds.

MOTHER: You can sit on your hands.
You can sit on your head.
But never, no, never
Look under the bed.

196

LEONARD: Who wants to swing
On the end of a vine?
And who wants to slide
On the end of a line?
I want to go now
And look under my bed.
That's where I must look
For the book I have read.

GRANDMOTHER: Sit down now, Leonard.
Sit here. Do not look.
Your mother and I
Will go find your book.

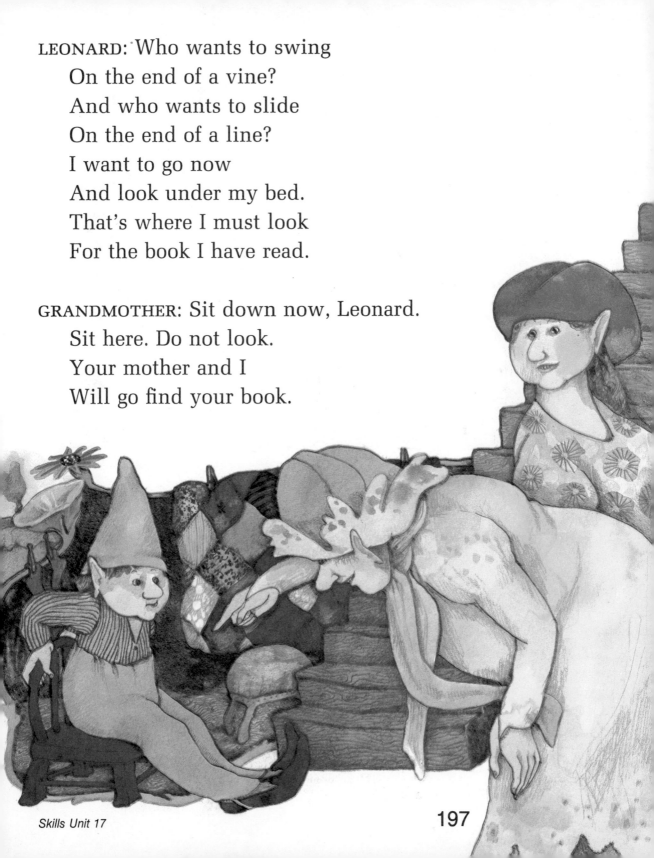

Pam looked at Leonard.
Here's what she said.

PAM: What is the secret
That's under the bed?

LEONARD: Grandmother knows.
What can it be?
What is the secret
That we cannot see?

198

MOTHER: We found it! We found it!
    It's blue and it's red.

LEONARD: You found my book.
    Was it under the bed?

GRANDMOTHER: Leonard, oh, Leonard,
    Keep this in your head.
    You must never, no, never
    Look under the bed!
    . . . until tomorrow.

Comprehension Check

1. What is under the bed?
2. What made Grandmother tell Leonard
    not to look under the bed?

The Three Goats

a Scandinavian tale

adapted by Regina Neuman

In a place far away from here, there was
a boy who had three goats.
Day after day the boy would take his goats
to a hill.

At the end of the day, the boy would call
out, and the goats would come down from
the hill.
Then the boy would take the goats home.

200

One day the boy called to the goats.
But the goats would not come.
The boy began to cry.
Soon two big birds came flying by.

"What are you crying about?" asked the
birds.

The boy said, "I am crying because the
goats will not come away from those
flowers."

"We will help you," said the birds.
And the two big birds did all they could
to help the boy.
But the goats would not come away from
the flowers.
So the birds began to cry too.
Next a fox came by.

"What are you crying about?" asked the
fox.

"We are crying because the boy is
crying," said the birds.
"And the boy is crying because the goats
will not come away from the flowers."

"I'll get the goats to come away," said
the fox.

And the fox did all it could to help the
boy.
But the goats would not come away from
the flowers.
So the fox began to cry too.

Last of all a small bee came by.
"What are you crying about?" asked the
bee.

The fox said, "I am crying because the
birds are crying.
The birds are crying because the boy
is crying.
And the boy is crying because the goats
will not come away from those flowers."

"I will get those goats to come away,"
said the bee.

"If we could not do it, a little bee like
you can't do it," said the animals.

"Look and see," the bee said.

Then the bee went flying over to the
goats.

"Look out! Look out for the bee!" the goats said.

Soon after that the bee was on its way home.
So were the goats.

Comprehension Check
1. What made the boy cry?
2. What did the bee do to get the goats to go home?

Bonus Unit

Bees

by Marchette Chute

I don't like bees
    As a general thing
When they sit down hard
    And start to sting.

But I like their song,
    And I like to lie
On the warm June ground
    When the bees go by.

Lunch at the Zoo

by Michael Bonadies

Yesterday the big elephant and the little
elephant ate lunch in their home.
Today both elephants want to have lunch
with their friends, the tiger and the seal.

208

Lunchtime came.

The little elephant put some peanuts into a small bag.

He put the bag upon his head.

The big elephant put four dishes into a box.

She put the box upon her head.

Both elephants walked to the far end of the zoo.

PARK

The elephants looked into the Seal House.
Then they looked into the Tiger House.
But their friends were not there.
Both elephants went into the park.
And there they found their friends.

210

The elephants started to take the lunch
out.
Both the seal and the tiger wanted to
help.

"Thank you, but there is not much work to
do," both elephants said.
"Play and have fun.
Soon we will have a nice lunch."

The big elephant put the dishes upon the
table.
The little elephant put the peanuts upon
the dishes.

"Time for lunch," said the little
elephant.
"Come and sit down."

The animals sat down to eat.

The tiger said, "I don't eat peanuts.
I eat meat."

The seal said, "I don't eat peanuts.
I eat fish."

The elephants did not know what to do.

Then the tiger and the seal both said,
"We want to go home."
And they ran home.

212

Soon the elephants saw the tiger and the seal.
The tiger had some meat.
The seal had a fish.
The tiger and the seal put their food
upon the dishes.
They gave all the peanuts to the
elephants.

"That's better," they both said.
"Now we can all eat."

And they all ate their lunch.

The seal ate all of his fish.
The tiger ate all of her meat.
And the elephants ate <u>all</u> of the peanuts.
Soon there was no more food upon the dishes.

"What a good lunch," they all said.

"Tomorrow we will make lunch for you," said the seal and the tiger.

Comprehension Check

1. What made the elephants ask the tiger and the seal to lunch?
2. What do elephants eat?
   What do tigers eat?
   What do seals eat?

Leave Herbert Alone

by Alma Marshak Whitney

Everybody was always telling Jennifer to leave Herbert alone.

"Leave Herbert alone," said her mother.

"Leave Herbert alone," said her brother.

"Leave Herbert alone," said her father.

Herbert was the cat next door.
He was big and had a fat, bushy tail.
Jennifer liked him.
She wanted to play with him.

But every time Herbert saw Jennifer
coming, he ran away.
He didn't walk away.
He ran as fast as he could.
And that made Jennifer feel bad.

Once Jennifer was playing with her drum.
She saw Herbert sitting on the sidewalk.
Jennifer was so happy to see him that she
dropped her drum with a crash and yelled,
"Herbert!"

216

Herbert turned and ran like mad.

"Leave Herbert alone," said her father.

Another time Jennifer was passing
Herbert's house when she saw him eating
a leaf on his lawn.
She started to run to him.

Herbert didn't waste any time.
He jumped into the bushes next to his
house.

"Leave Herbert alone," said her brother.

Then there was the time that Jennifer
tried to catch Herbert.
She hid behind a tree and waited for him
to walk by.
And as soon as he did Jennifer jumped out
and grabbed him.
"HERBERT!" she screamed.
Herbert jumped out of her hands and ran
away.

One day Jennifer was sitting on her front
steps eating a tuna-fish sandwich.
She saw Herbert walking by.
Jennifer got up, but then she sat down.

"He'll just run away," she thought.

Herbert saw Jennifer.
He got ready to run.

Jennifer looked at Herbert.
She didn't want anybody to hear her so
she said very, very quietly, "Hi,
Herbert."

Herbert sat down right in front of her!
Jennifer looked at Herbert.
Herbert looked at Jennifer.
Nobody moved.
Not even a little bit.
Jennifer felt very happy.

"Herbert, come here, Herbert."

Herbert came a little closer.

220

Very slowly, Jennifer took a little piece of tuna fish in her hand and held it out to Herbert.

"Here, Herbert," she said softly.

Herbert looked up and started sniffing. He came a little closer to Jennifer.

Jennifer sat as still as she could with the piece of tuna fish in her hand. And all of a sudden, Herbert licked the piece of tuna fish right out of Jennifer's hand!

Oh, was Jennifer happy!
She picked her hand up very slowly and
put it down very gently on Herbert's
head.

Herbert made a sound.
"Purr, purr, purr."
Then Herbert jumped up on the step next
to Jennifer and rubbed his furry head on
her knee.

Now nobody has to tell Jennifer to
leave Herbert alone anymore.

222

MASTERY WORD LIST

The following high-frequency words (words that appear on recognized word-frequency lists) have been read a minimum of six times by the end of this book. Pupils should be able to recognize both the root word and the root word with these endings: s, es, ed, ing, and 's.

The page number printed after each word in the following list shows the word's first appearance in this book. The list on page 224 is a cumulative list of previously mastered words.

park	9	than	45	don't	81	eat	149
bird	17	grow	49	say	81	drink	149
he	23	little	49	start	82	so	150
ask	23	best	49	open	82	way	150
she	24	better	50	walk	82	any	154
made	24	need	51	here	84	went	161
dog	25	these	51	talk	84	home	164
funny	25	no	51	man	87	were	164
one	29	too	51	began	89	saw	164
day	29	much	51	live	97	those	171
am	29	if	52	kind	97	small	172
some	29	how	55	draw	99	stop	173
will	29	class	55	line	99	wind	178
orange	30	us	55	happy	112	off	179
had	30	same	55	pretty	112	found	186
purple	31	up	57	be	112	buy	186
an	32	Father	61	after	121	Mr.	186
last	41	first	63	soon	122	Mrs.	186
more	41	was	65	Mother	124	which	189
two	42	cut	70	ran	124	must	194
three	42	feet	71	great	127	never	195
four	42	many	71	as	131	sit	195
five	42	hands	72	side	132	cry	201
six	42	head	73	today	142	ate	208
seven	42	time	75	take	143	both	208
eight	42	give	76	call	144	their	208
gave	42	ride	76	thank	144	into	209
got	42	his	76	pull	144	upon	209

a	far	light	the
about	find	like	there
all	fly	look	they
and	for	make	thing
animal	get	me	this
are	giant	my	to
at	girl	name	together
away	go	new	told
behind	going	not	under
big	good	now	want
blue	green	on	wash
book	has	out	we
box	have	over	what
boy	help	people	where
but	her	play	who
by	house	put	wish
came	I	red	with
can	I'll	run	work
can't	in	said	would
cold	is	see	yard
come	it	shop	yellow
could	jump	sing	you
did	know	something	your
do	land	table	zoo
down	laugh	that	